Look! Long Ta
And Tall Tales
In one of the p
Some witches a
In others are ogres
And wise men and kings,
And one has a Dreamer
Who wishes for wings.
There's magic and mischief
And mermaids and more –
Like genies and giants
And dragons galore.
So if you want wizards
And pirates, just look –
They're all to be found
In this fabulous book!

Other poetry titles published by Corgi books:

Anthologies
A POT OF GOLD edited by Jill Bennett
A STACK OF STORY POEMS edited byTony Bradman
A GERBIL IN THE HOOVER by Jerome Fletcher

Poetry Picture Books
BAGS OF POEMS: FAMILY ALBUM
edited by Jill Bennett, illustrated by Sami Sweeten

BAGS OF POEMS: A JUMBLE OF CLOTHES
edited by Jill Bennett, illustrated by Sue Heap

JUNGLE JINGLES AND OTHER ANIMAL POEMS
by Dick King-Smith, illustrated by Jonathan Allen

Long Tales, Short Tales and Tall Tales

Poems and Pictures by Colin West

CORGI BOOKS

LONG TALES, SHORT TALES AND TALL TALES
A CORGI BOOK : 0 552 52798 X

First published in Great Britain by Doubleday, 1995

PRINTING HISTORY
Doubleday edition published 1995
Corgi edition published 1996

© 1995 Colin West

'Connie and her Unicorn' first appeared in *Ten Golden Years*,
Walker Books, 1989, and is used by permission
'The Natty Knight Sir Nigel' first appeared in *A Stack of Story Poems*,
Doubleday, 1992

The right of Colin West to be identified as the Author and
Illustrator of this work has been asserted in accordance with
the Copyright, Designs and Patents Act 1988.

Corgi Books are published by Transworld Publishers Ltd,
61–63 Uxbridge Road, Ealing, London W5 5SA,
in Australia by Transworld Publishers (Australia) Pty Ltd,
15–25 Helles Avenue, Moorebank, NSW 2170,
and in New Zealand by Transworld Publishers (NZ) Ltd,
3 William Pickering Drive, Albany, Auckland.

Printed and bound in Great Britain by
Cox & Wyman Ltd, Reading, Berkshire

Contents

Connie and Her Unicorn

Early one white winter's morn
Came Connie and her unicorn.
She knocked upon the great front door
Of greedy giant Gobblemore.

The giant, stirring in his bed,
Rubbed both his eyes and scratched his
 head.
'Who is it dares wake Gobblemore?'
He roared whilst answering the door.
And who should stand there all forlorn,
But Connie and her unicorn.
(Now, though he'd gorged the night before,
He hungered still, did Gobblemore;
Thought he, 'Oh, unicorns are sweet,
And how I yearn to eat that meat!')
So, 'Dear child, please come in!' he cried.
And thus did Connie go inside.

Her face was thin, her clothes were torn,
But plumpish was her unicorn.
'Dear child, what have you come here for?'
Asked the sly giant, Gobblemore.
(And as he spoke, he noticed that
Her unicorn was nice and fat!)
'Oh sir, I'm sorry,' Connie said,
'I come to beg a crust of bread.
I have no money, but I trust
You'll let me have a little crust.'
Said Gobblemore (who wasn't kind
And had but one thought in his mind):
'If you've no gold to pay the debt,
Just let me have that freakish pet!'

At such a thought the girl felt sad –
Her unicorn was all she had –
But as she hung her head in woe,
She saw she had no choice, and so
Although her heart was sadly torn,
She sighed, 'Farewell, my unicorn.'
And with these words, she swapped her
    beast
For one extremely frugal feast –
Her crust of bread was far from large
And spread with just the merest marge.

Meanwhile, the giant scoured a book
To see the nicest way to cook
A unicorn; fried, boiled or stewed,
Or grilled or baked or barbecued?

When Connie saw the giant take
Her unicorn away to bake,
She realized at once his aim
And thought she'd try and stop his game.
She grabbed a saucepan from a shelf
And closed her eyes and braced herself,
Then flung it, hardly thinking that
She'd hit him, but she knocked him flat!

With Gobblemore now out stone cold,
Shy Connie was a bit more bold:
She dragged the giant round the floor
And kicked him out his own back door,
Then pushed him to the icy well,
And made quite sure that in he fell.

Then with her unicorn she went
And raided his establishment:
They ate up all that they could find
And didn't leave a scrap behind –
Ate every leg of beef and ham,
And every slice of bread and jam,
And every beetroot, every bean –
They even licked their platters clean.
And every goblet, every cup,
They drank them down and drank them up.

It took all day and half the night
To eat up everything in sight,
And when at last they both were sure
There really wasn't any more,
They left, full up, at crack of dawn,
Did Connie and her unicorn.

14

The Three Highwaymen

In Hampstead lived three highwaymen
As haughty as could be,
And as to who was handsomest,
They never would agree,
For each one thought, 'The prettiest
Undoubtedly is *me*!'

Said Sam, 'I have a noble nose
That makes me look refined!'
Said Sid, 'My flowing flaxen hair
Leaves all the rest behind!'
Said Saul, 'No, it's my sparkling eyes –
They're of the wondrous kind!'

In Hampstead thus the ruffians,
They bickered day and night,
Until at last they all agreed
To find out who was right:
They planned the hold-up of a coach,
Quite soon, in broad daylight;

And furthermore, they all agreed,
To make complete the task,
When having robbed the passengers,
They'd each remove their mask.
Then, 'Who's the handsomest of all?'
The passengers they'd ask.

Thought Sam, 'They'll see my noble nose
And say I'm so refined!'

Thought Sid, 'They'll see my flaxen hair,
That leaves the rest behind!'

Thought Saul, 'They'll see my sparkling eyes
Are of the wondrous kind!'

And so it was on Saturday,
Ten minutes after noon,
They stopped a coach on Hampstead Heath

And plundered from it soon;
Then as they each pulled off their mask,
Oh, how the folk did swoon!

The highwaymen were quite perplexed
To see the people faint,
But thought, 'It must be ecstasy,
The cause of this complaint.
We all three must be beautiful!'
They laughed without restraint.

And satisfied, they galloped home,
Where they spent several days
Gazing in the mirror through
A sort of rosy haze,
And flattering each other too,
With tender words of praise.

But posters soon were pasted up
Enquiring, *Have you seen*
Three highwaymen — one with a nose
Shaped like a runner bean,
Another who has haystack hair,
And one whose eyes look mean?

A Princess Called Pauline

There once was a princess called Pauline,
And under a tarpaulin awning
She sat on the shoreline each morning,
And spent it in stretching and yawning,
Whilst catching the crabs that were crawling
Beside her, beneath the tarpaulin.

One Sunday, a fisherman trawling
For salmon nearby sighted Pauline,
And thought her the loveliest Fräulein
He'd spotted for many a morning.

He went to her tarpaulin awning
Without even giving a warning,

And said, 'You appeal to me, Pauline,
Forgive me, I beg you, for calling,
But for you I'm hopelessly falling.'

Still Pauline continued in yawning
And didn't acknowledge his fawning.

The fisherman, blubbing and bawling,
Returned to the business of trawling,
As Pauline, with manners appalling,
Went back to the crabs that were crawling
Beside her, beneath the tarpaulin.

The Carpet with a Hole

Once a merchant in a market
Showed a tatty-looking carpet
To a rather foolish fellow.
It was purple, pink and yellow
With a big hole in the middle
(Which seemed something of a fiddle!)

But this fellow still adored it,
And could just about afford it,
So he bought that tatty carpet
And he took it from the market
To a faraway oasis
(One of his most favourite places),
And that carpet with a hole in
He was presently unrollin'.

It was damp and it was dusty
And it smelled a little musty,
But to that misguided fellow
It seemed mystical and mellow;
Though the middle bit was perished,
That old carpet still he cherished,
So he thought he'd sit upon it
And compose a little sonnet
All about that tatty carpet
Which he'd purchased from the market.

(Notice how the hole is fitting
Round him, in the middle, sitting.)

Holey rug, you have a beauty
Far beyond the call of duty . . .
Thus he scribbled with his biro.
Meanwhile, somewhere south of Cairo,
There appeared a change of weather:
Little breezes blew together
And in strength they started growing
Till one mighty blast was blowing . . .

Over rooftops, over fountains,
Over deserts, over mountains,
It came swishing, it came swooshing,
It came whishing, it came whooshing,
Bending trees and blowing camels
Off their feet, the poor old mammals.

Who'd have thought a breeze on high would
Sweep that holey carpet skyward?
But it did – with one great bluster
Up it went! Just like a duster
High above, the carpet fluttered!
Back on earth the fellow muttered:
'Mercy me! It's truly tragic,
For that carpet's clearly magic.
I'd be flying single-handed
If it hadn't left me stranded.
I'd be swooping like a swallow
If that rug had not been hollow,
But as I composed my idyll,
I was sitting in the middle –
Where that hole was all around me –
Such calamities confound me!'

As he spoke, the carpet vanished,
And to Who-Knows-Where was banished.

No more did he see that carpet.
Did it blow back to the market?
Was it on a secret mission?
Was the merchant some magician?
Did the hole have mystic powers?
One could contemplate for hours
What became of that old carpet
Which was purchased in the market;
But that carpet in whose middle
Was a hole, remains a riddle.

The Natty Knight Sir Nigel

Sir Nigel was a natty knight
Who liked to keep his armour bright.
He polished up his suit of metal
Till shiny as a copper kettle.
(It took a lot of elbow grease
To polish each and every piece.)

When other knights went off to wars,
Sir Nigel could be found indoors;
While other knights their foes demolished,
Sir Nigel just stayed home and polished;
And every nut and bolt and screw
All came up looking good as new.

Now, one day, when some other knights
Returned from gruesome battle sites,
They thought they might be welcomed home,
But Nigel just cried, 'Mind my chrome!
It's bright and shiny, not like yours,
That's scuffed and scratched through
    fighting wars!'

Of course, his fellow knights were vexed
And wondered what he might say next.
Sir Nigel, having thought a bit,
Then added, 'While I think of it,
I hope no-one expects to borrow
My metal-cleaning stuff tomorrow!'
Then just to show he was well bred,
He said, 'Good-night' and went to bed.

Sir John, Sir Jasper and Sir Paul
Were dumbstruck by Sir Nigel's gall.
Sir Hector and Sir Ethelred
Could scarce believe the things he'd said.
Sir Desmond and Sir Dominic
Were left there, feeling pretty sick.

Now, when they'd gathered up their wits,
Said John: 'We mustn't call it quits!'
They sat and wondered what to do
To bring him down a peg or two.
They pondered hard and by next day
Between them, they'd worked out a way.

They made a great big dragon skin
From bits of wood and glass and tin.
They made it tall enough and wide
For all of them to fit inside.

Great puffs of purple smoke came out
The nostrils each side of its snout.
Its mouth was fearsome, breathing flame,
Its teeth were sharp, its claws the same.
Its handsome green umbrella wings
Were realistic-looking things.
Its fourteen legs had lots of scales,
Its bottom was as hard as nails.
In short, it was a ghastly sight,
Enough to give grown men a fright,
Not least of all Sir Nigel, who
Was scared of spiders in the loo.

The seven knights thus underneath
The dragon costume, with its teeth
And claws and scales and fiery breath,
Thought they'd scare Nigel half to death,
And even if he wasn't hurt,
At least he'd grovel in the dirt
And spoil his spotless suit of steel,
And what a fool he's bound to feel
When he finds out it's all a hoax
And just one of their little jokes!

They waited for Sir Nigel, knowing
That soon to market he'd be going
To buy a tin of Duraglit
As he was getting short of it.
With bated breath at half–past three
They hid behind a chestnut tree,
And tittered to themselves and thought,
'Oh, what a lesson he'll be taught!'

36

Quite soon Sir Nigel came in sight,
Proud in his suit of armour bright.
Just as he passed the chestnut tree
The 'dragon' jumped out suddenly:
Like something from a nasty dream
It looked, and boy, did Nigel scream!

But then one knight, Sir Ethelred,
Inside the dragon's hollow head,
Whose job it was to work the smoke,
Inhaled some and began to choke,
And then with one almighty cough
He blew the costume's head clean off!

Sir Nigel, who was much surprised
To see this face he recognized,
Then saw it all was but a game –
The mighty monster now seemed tame:
A dragon who had lost its head
And got a human one instead!
Sir Nigel laughed and cried, 'Baloney!
This monster's nothing but a phoney!'

The seven knights were rather miffed
Their clever plan had gone adrift,
And went home without much to say
As Nigel went his merry way.

This could have been the way it ends,
But no, the road was full of bends.
The outcome couldn't be forlorner:
Behind a rock around the corner
A real-life dragon (looking thinner
Than it ought, through lack of dinner)
Was waiting for some poor dimwit
To come by, to be ate by it . . .

Sir Nigel came, he saw, he giggled.
Sir Nigel got the dragon niggled.
He thought: 'This dragon's also fake,'
Which was, of course, a grave mistake.
He laughed aloud until he buckled.
'I'll not be fooled again!' he chuckled.

The dragon couldn't see the joke,
And breathing fire and belching smoke,
It opened up its jaws and ate
Sir Nigel and his armour plate.

The Fair Witch

There once was a witch
And she wore a tall hat,
She rode on a broomstick
And kept a black cat;
She did all the things
You'd expect of a witch –
Like looking for lizards
And frogs in a ditch,
Then throwing them into
A bubbling brew –
In short, all the things
You'd expect her to do.

But wait for a minute,
Don't think that this witch
Was humdrum – she wasn't –
For here comes the hitch:
Although she was evil
And ever so mean,
This witch had the loveliest
Face you have seen.

This witch, she was pretty,
This witch, she was fair;
This witch had the silkiest
Shimmering hair;
Her chin wasn't pointed,
Her nose wasn't bent,

And people admired her
Wherever she went.
And this was most useful,
For she could befriend
Folk whom she'd otherwise
Only offend,
Then when she had charmed them,
She'd suddenly go
And change them to meatballs
And large lumps of dough.

(With meatballs so juicy
And dumplings so fat,
She'd make a fine stew
For herself and her cat.)

44

The other bad witches
Thought all this unfair:
'You can't have a witch
Who has beautiful hair!
A witch should be ugly
With hair black as jet
And the sort of a face
That you'll never forget.
You know where you stand
With somebody who looks
Just like all the pictures
Of witches in books,
But as for this Fair Witch,
It doesn't seem right
To see her deceive
People every night –
People who would, if
They saw one of *us*,
Go running away
Twice the speed of a bus!'

So this is what happened
One evening in June:
They grabbed the Fair Witch
Beneath the full moon;

And these are the spells
That they chanted at her
To make her as ugly
As they themselves were:

'Fiddledee, Fiddledum,
What if your nose
Was big as a beetroot
And red as a rose!'

'Gobbledee, Gobblegum,
What if your head
Was fat as a pumpkin
That's very well fed!'

'Crickledee, Crickledum,
What if your feet
Were flat and were wide
As two platefuls of meat!'

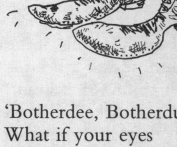

'Botherdee, Botherdum,
What if your eyes
Were two ripe tomatoes
Amazing in size!'

And as they all spluttered
Each devilish spell,
The Fair Witch just smiled,
For she knew very well
That when any witch
Tries *another* to curse,
The spell will backfire,
And she'll come off the worse;
And this is what happened
Before very long,
When all of their witchcraft
Went woefully wrong:
For every bad witch
Became uglier still,
Their faces and bodies
Transforming, until
Their eyes were tomatoes,
And as for their feet,
Each hideous witch
Had two platefuls of meat;
Each nose was a beetroot,
A pumpkin, each head,
And so shocked they were,
That they all dropped down dead!

Just one witch was standing
And kept smiling through –
The Fair Witch, who now made
Her best-ever stew –
It filled every bowl
And it filled every cup:
How she and her cat
Enjoyed lapping it up!

Fred's Fantastic Boots

Long years ago, or so it's said,
There lived a peasant, name of Fred,
Who had a secret sort of passion
For footwear in the latest fashion.
Fred longed for shoes of shiny leather
With heels that he could click together;
He longed for slippers made of suede
And sandals trimmed with silver braid;
But most of all (much more than *those*),
He longed for boots with pointed toes.

But Fred was poor, and being such,
Could not afford to purchase much –
He only had a single pair
Of worn-out wooden clogs to wear.

Fred looked in each outfitter's shop
Whenever he had time to stop,
And marvelled at the rows and rows
Of boots with long and curly toes,
Till one day, tearing out his hair,
He vowed, 'I'll make myself a pair!'

Fred gathered little scraps of leather
And neatly stitched them all together;
He made the sole, the heel, the upper,
And seldom stopped to have a 'cuppa';
He worked till late (and got up early)
To make the toes both long and curly.
At last he'd fashioned for each foot
A multi-coloured patchwork boot,
With pointed toes so elongated
That Fred felt quite exhilarated;
Then on the tip of either toe
He fixed a bell that tinkled so.

Fred held the boots and slipped them on,
And thought his sorrows now were gone!
He went out feeling really proud,
Quite unaware 'twas not allowed
For peasants such as Fred to sport
Boots of the long and curly sort.
As Fred marched on, with each new stride
He felt a greater sense of pride;
When he was coming, folk could tell –
They heard the tinkle of a bell.
Fred proudly thought, 'They must admire
My feet in such comely attire!'

He pranced about the village green
(The best place to be heard and seen).
Some people clapped, some people
   cheered,
Some others made rude signs and jeered;
Some shouted, some said not a word,
But on one point they all concurred:
The young, the middle-aged, the wrinkled,
All laughed to hear the way he tinkled.

Of course, it wasn't long before
Poor Fred was pulled up by the law:
Some soldiers saw his curly toes
And cried, 'You can't wear boots like
  those.
You have to be at least an earl
To wear a boot with such a twirl.'

They hauled him off before the king
As Fred cried, 'Help! What's happening?'

The king, for his part, scratched his head.
'Who made those boots?' he asked of Fred.
'I did myself,' replied the peasant,
'But you may have them as a present.'
(Fred clearly wasn't quite as daft
As thought those folk who jeered and
    laughed.)

At once the king put on the boots
And let out several happy hoots.

56

How joyous was His Majesty –
The footwear fitted perfectly!
'These are the finest boots on earth!'
The monarch marvelled in his mirth.
He danced and tinkled round the garden,
And granted Fred a Royal Pardon.

What's more, there's just one other thing,
He made Fred 'Cobbler to the King'.

Mary the Mixed-up Mermaid

Now, once upon a time there was a mermaid
Who looked just like her sisters of the sea,
Above her tummy button being human,
Below it being fishy as can be.

But Mary was a restless sort of mermaid,
Who didn't care for salty spray or foam.

She longed to live beside a yellow cornfield
Upon a hill, where she might feel at home.

Each night she slept beneath the dancing
    moonbeams,
And dreamed of picking pears and climbing
    trees;
She dreamed of doing cartwheels in the
    clover,
And keeping seven hives of honey bees.

One day upon the rocks she sat
   daydreaming,
When suddenly an octopus appeared.
To her amazement, up it crawled beside
   her,
And whispered words which sounded
   rather weird.

It said, 'Galumph! Begorra! and Bedraggle!'
It said, 'Balloo! Hooray! and Jamboree!'
It then arose, and with a funny totter,
It wibble-wobbled back into the sea.

I can't say what those words meant that it
  mumbled,
But somehow Mary seemed to understand.
From that day on, she swims around
  contented,
And dreams no more of living on the land.

The Tale of a Pig

Near Stratford Town in days gone by,
There lived some piggies in a sty;
The youngest of this merry brood
Was not too fond of piggy food:
The stuff he didn't care to scoff
With other piggies at the trough,
For Francis was a special pig,
Whose snout was small, but brain was big.

All day he sat and overheard
Each passing stranger's every word,
And everything he heard them say,
Inside his head he stored away.
He built up quite a large amount
Of words, which he would then recount,
First in his head, then feeling proud,
Some of them he'd recite aloud.
It wasn't long before this porker
Had turned into a super talker!

The human chap who came each day
At feeding time, stood in dismay
When first he heard young Francis mutter
Things *he* thought that no beast should
    utter.
He bent down low and cocked an ear,
The better for the pig to hear,
Then flabbergasted, shook his head,
As once again young Francis said:
'The pigswill stinks, and what is more,
The pigsty needs a new front door.'

Amazed, he cried, 'A pig who talks!
Before my eyes he breathes and walks!
This piggy surely is a beast
Who must be worth ten pounds at least!'

He clapped his hands and danced a jig
To come across so rare a pig,
Then went home laughing all the way:
'Tomorrow will be Market Day!'

When next day dawned, he came around,
And carted Francis off to town.
He took him to the Market Square,
And showed him to the people there.
Soon there was gathered quite a crowd
To hear the pig who talked aloud!

A farmer offered two pounds ten,
Another bid six guineas, then
A fellow came right up and said:
'My niece, named Anne, is soon to wed.
What better present than a pig?
Upon my waistcoat and my wig,
I'll give you seven bags of gold!'
At which the pigman hollered, 'SOLD!'

And thus did Francis come to be
Part of a human family.
He learned to eat with knife and fork,
And to improve his gift of talk.

Gadzooks!
This meal is
most agreeable!

He got on with his masters well –
They taught him how to count and spell,
And as he was so very bright,
They taught him how to read and write.

He wrote a sonnet every day,
Anne's acts of kindness to repay,
And every now and then a play
He put her husband William's way.

He died at last aged eighty-nine,
And everybody mourned the swine.
Correct me, now, if I'm mistaken,
But that's the tale of Francis Bacon.

Percy the Pirate

When people think of pirates,
They think of strapping men
With cutlasses and whiskers,
And names like Jake or Ben.

But Percy was a pirate
More fearsome than the rest,
Although he had no muscles
Or hairs upon his chest.

For Percy's secret weapon
No brute could ever beat,

He never was without it –
His pair of smelly feet.

When he was out marauding,
His foes he would out-fox
By rapidly removing
His boots, and then his socks.

And then he'd do a handstand
And wave his feet aloft,
And so upon the ozone
The whiff would gently waft.

His victims' eyes would water,
Their noses, they would sniff,

Then fulsomely the fellows
Would catch the pungent whiff.

And falling down like nine-pins,
They'd all be knocked out cold,
Then Percy would relieve them
Of jewellery and gold.

Yes, Percy was the pirate
No brute could ever beat,
Who owned a ton of treasure
Thanks solely to his feet.

The Dreamer's Favourite Hat

Upon a grassy hillside sat
The Dreamer, in his favourite hat.
He dreamed one day that he might rise
Above the hills, into the skies,
To dip and dive, and soar and swoop
Like some bird in a flying troupe.

It was from such a reverie
The Dreamer woke up suddenly,
And saw a chap in starry clothes,
A wacky wizard, strange as those
You see in books or puppet shows,
Complete with beard and great big nose.

The Wizard said, 'How do you do!
I'll make your greatest wish come true.'
Now, who could have said 'no' to that?
The Dreamer, taking off his hat,
Politely said, 'Upon my word,
I wish that I could be a bird –
I'd love to be a swallow, or
A swift, so I could swoop and soar!'
The Wizard, grinning like a cat,
Offered to take the Dreamer's hat,
Then having placed it on his head,
He waved his arms till he went red.

What happened next was really weird:
A magic-looking star appeared.
The Dreamer felt his arms grow longer,
He felt his muscles getting stronger;
But then his knees felt weak as water
As he watched both his legs grow shorter.

The Wizard waved a great amount
And made more stars than you could
   count,
And as the stars fell thick and fast,
The Dreamer was a bird at last!
His chest was decked in feathers brown,
His tummy turned to eiderdown.
He scarcely could believe such things,
Until he flapped his new-found wings,
And found, indeed, that he could fly
And join the birdies up on high.

It's true he wasn't quite a swift,
More like a duck who'd gone adrift,
But never having quite been slim,
A duck was good enough for him.

For hours that fine summer's day,
He took part in an air display.
He soon learned how to soar and swoop,
And even did a loop-the-loop.

He flew with pigeons, flapped with geese,
And thought his joy would never cease.
Then when his wings began to ache,
He glided down to take a break.

Upon the grassy slope he landed,
But sensed at once he'd been left stranded.
The Wizard with his nose and beard
Most thoughtlessly had disappeared.
The Dreamer sobbed and wondered how
He could again be human now.
What made the matter worse, was that
He'd also lost his favourite hat.
He sought the Wizard, but in vain –
He never saw his like again.

For seven nights and seven days
The Dreamer followed bird-like ways:
He dined on snails and worms and flies,
And glumly flew about the skies.
He cared no more to swoop and soar,
The whole thing had become a bore.
But then one day, this man-turned-duck
Had an amazing stroke of luck:
He spotted something in a tree,
And asked himself, 'Pray, can it be
The favourite hat I used to wear?'
And saw it *was* as he got near.

He flew down to retrieve his hat,
Which now was tattered, squashed and flat;
The thing he gaily dusted down,
And soon reshaped its crumpled crown.
Then as he brushed its battered brim,
A hopeful thought occurred to him:
'The Wizard wore this hat of mine –
Perhaps some magic's left behind!'

He wildly waved the hat about.
Lo and behold! A star fell out!
'Yippee!' the Dreamer cried in glee,
'There's still some magic left for me!'

Again he waved the hat around,
Another star fell to the ground.
He made a wish, the end result
Of which, was he began to moult,
Then as more magic stars appeared,
He looked a lot less like a bird.

His wings grew short, his legs grew fat,
As stars still tumbled from his hat.
And when no more fell out, why then,
He saw he was a man again!

And now the Dreamer can be found
With both feet firmly on the ground.
And as for having been a bird,
He utters not a single word.
His secret's safe, and that is that –
He keeps it underneath his hat.

Young King Cole

In days gone by, there lived a king
Who wasn't pleased with anything,
And nothing made him laugh or sing;
No, nothing made him sing.

His every duty seemed a chore,
His orchestra he found a bore,
His jester's jokes he'd heard before,
He'd heard them all before.

I say,
I say,
I say...

He called his wise men and he said,
'I hate this crown upon my head,
Can't I be something else instead,
Be something else instead?'

His wise men (very clever chaps)
At once put on their thinking caps,
And when they'd thought, they said, 'Perhaps,'
They said to him, 'Perhaps . . .

'Your Majesty could be a knight
And learn to joust and fence and fight,
And kill off dragons left and right,
Kill dragons left and right!'

The king turned pale and shook his head,
'I don't like dragons much,' he said,
'Can't I be something else instead,
Be something else instead?'

The wise men (very clever chaps)
Again put on their thinking caps,
And when they'd thought, they said,
    'Perhaps,'
They said to him, 'Perhaps . . .

'Your Majesty would rather be
A sailor on the salty sea,
And swim with serpents wild and free,
With serpents wild and free!'

The king turned green and shook his head,
'I don't like water much,' he said,
'Can't I be something else instead,
Be something else instead?'

The wise men (very clever chaps)
Once more put on their thinking caps,
And when they'd thought, they said,
  'Perhaps,'
They said to him, 'Perhaps . . .

'Your Majesty could be a monk
And use the floorboards as a bunk,
And never more get roaring drunk,
No, never more get drunk!'

The king turned red and shook his head,
'I think I'll stay a king,' he said;
And with those words, he went to bed,
The king went off to bed.

The wise men (very clever chaps)
Said as they doffed their thinking caps,
'He's learned a lesson now, perhaps,
A lesson now, perhaps.'

And sure enough, next day the king
Who'd not been pleased with anything,
At last learned how to laugh and sing,
He learned to laugh and sing.

He grew into a merry soul,
Who called for fiddlers, pipe and bowl;
Let's sing a song of Old King Cole,
A song of Old King Cole!

Cricklewick Hall

I went to a party
At Cricklewick Hall:
The spooks and the spectres
Were having a ball;

The hostess, a ghostess,
She was, I am sure –
I noticed the moment
She walked through the door.

Dirty Cowboy Bert

Now, here's the tale of Cowboy Bert,
Who liked to roll around in dirt,
And never washed, or changed his shirt.

Whenever Bert went into town,
The people looked him up and down,
His dirty habits made them frown.

'Of all the cowboys in the West,
I surely am the dirtiest,
I'm much more dirty than the rest!'
Sang Dirty Cowboy Bert.

But then one day, when rolling round
Upon the dirty desert ground,
Of horses' hooves he heard the sound.

And looking up, what did he see?
The sheriff and his deputy,
Complete with posse one, two, three.

Bert didn't get the chance to run,
The sheriff calmly pulled a gun,
As did the others, one by one,
On Dirty Cowboy Bert.

They fired, when having taken aim,
But from their guns no bullets came,
For it was all a little game:

The guns were water pistols, so
Old Bert was drenched from head to toe
In nothing worse than H_2O.

And then the sheriff took a rope,
And skilfully lassoed the dope.
And handed a big bar of soap
To Dirty Cowboy Bert.

Bert had no choice, and so began
To soap himself all over, and
He soon was looking spick and span.

With Cowboy Bert now looking clean,
He didn't seem so big and mean –
Not half the man he once had been.

How they all laughed at Cowboy Bert,
And here's the thing that really hurt –
His nickname soon was *Little Squirt*,
Not Dirty Cowboy Bert.

A Genie in a Lamp

There lives a genie in a lamp
Who suffers dreadful from the cramp,
Above all, when the weather's damp,
And cries, 'Hey, let me out!'

The lamp he lives in, sad to say,
Lies in an attic, tucked away,
Where no-one ventures night or day
To ever hear him shout.

For centuries he's cried and cursed,
On rainy days he feels the worst,
And bellows till he's fit to burst,
While wriggling about.

You wonder how I come to be
Relating his sad history?
It's simple, for that genie's *me*,
Now won't you let me out?